BEST OF
LENNY KRAVITZ
FOR EASY GUITAR

Cover photography by Mark Seliger

ISBN 1-85909-995-5

IMP International Music Publications Limited
Griffin House 161 Hammersmith Road London W6 8BS England

Photo by Kevin Mazur

CONTENTS

Photo by Mark Seliger

BELIEVE

Words by Lenny Kravitz
Music by Lenny Kravitz and Henry Hirsch

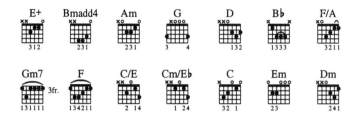

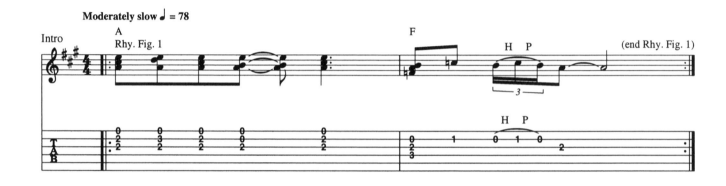

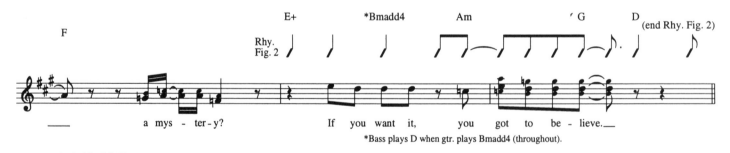

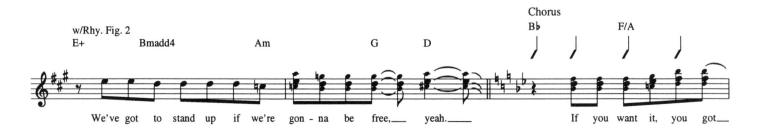

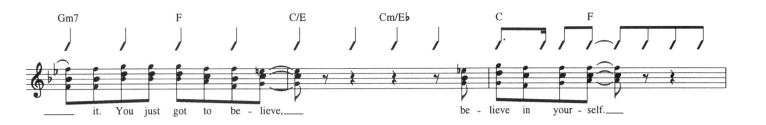

it. You just got to be-lieve,_____ be - lieve in your-self._____

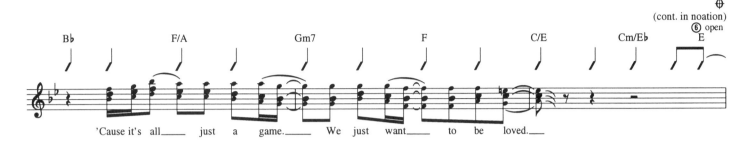

'Cause it's all_____ just a game._____ We just want_____ to be loved._____

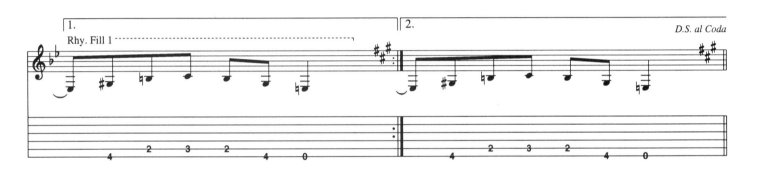

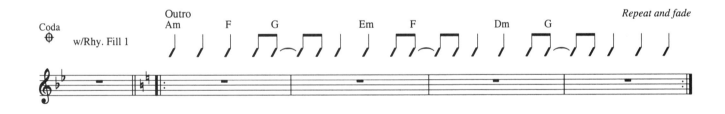

Additional Lyrics

3. The Son of God is in our face,
   Offering us eternal grace.
   If you want it, you got to believe.

4. 'Cause being free is a state of mind.
   We'll one day leave this all behind.
   Just put your faith in God, and one day you'll see, yeah. *(To Chorus)*

5. The future's in our present hands.
   Let's reach right in. Let's understand.
   If you want it, you got to believe, yeah. *(To Chorus)*

ARE YOU GONNA GO MY WAY

Words by Lenny Kravitz
Music by Lenny Kravitz and Craig Ross

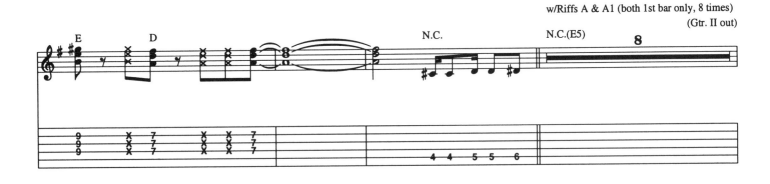

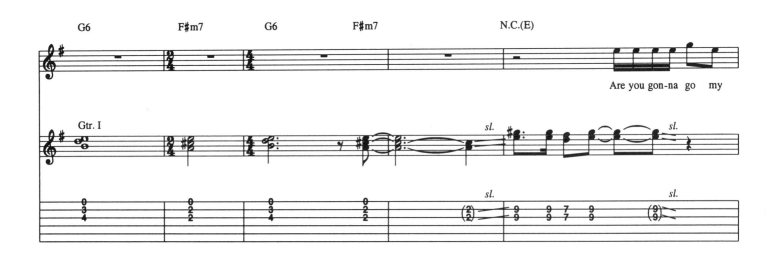

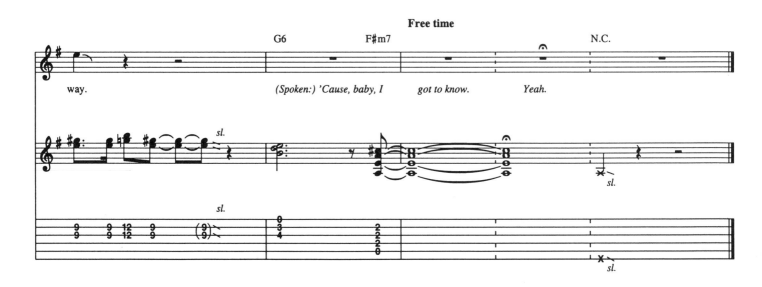

FLY AWAY

Words and Music by
Lenny Kravitz

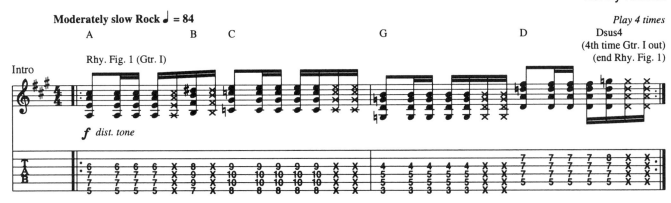

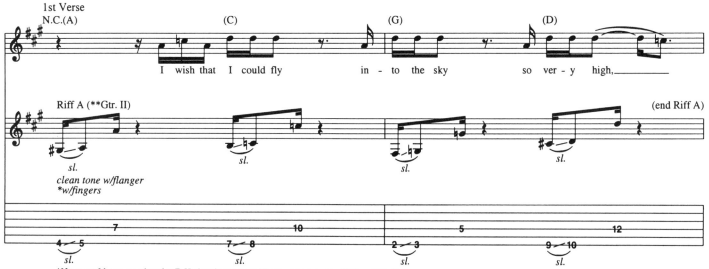

*Notes on 6th stg. are played w/R.H. thumb; notes on 4th stg. are snapped w/R.H. middle finger.
**Bass arr. for gtr.

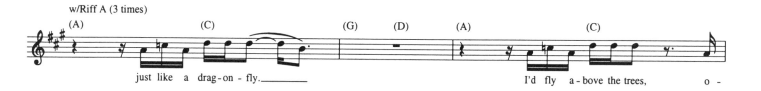

just like a drag-on-fly.___ I'd fly a-bove the trees, o-

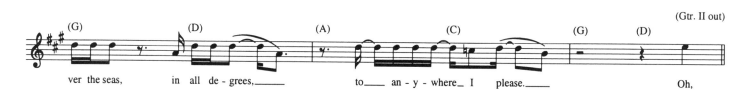

ver the seas, in all de-grees,___ to___ an-y-where_ I please.___ Oh,

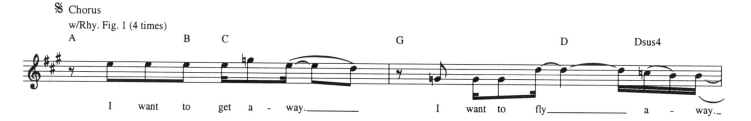

I want to get a-way.___ I want to fly___ a-way.

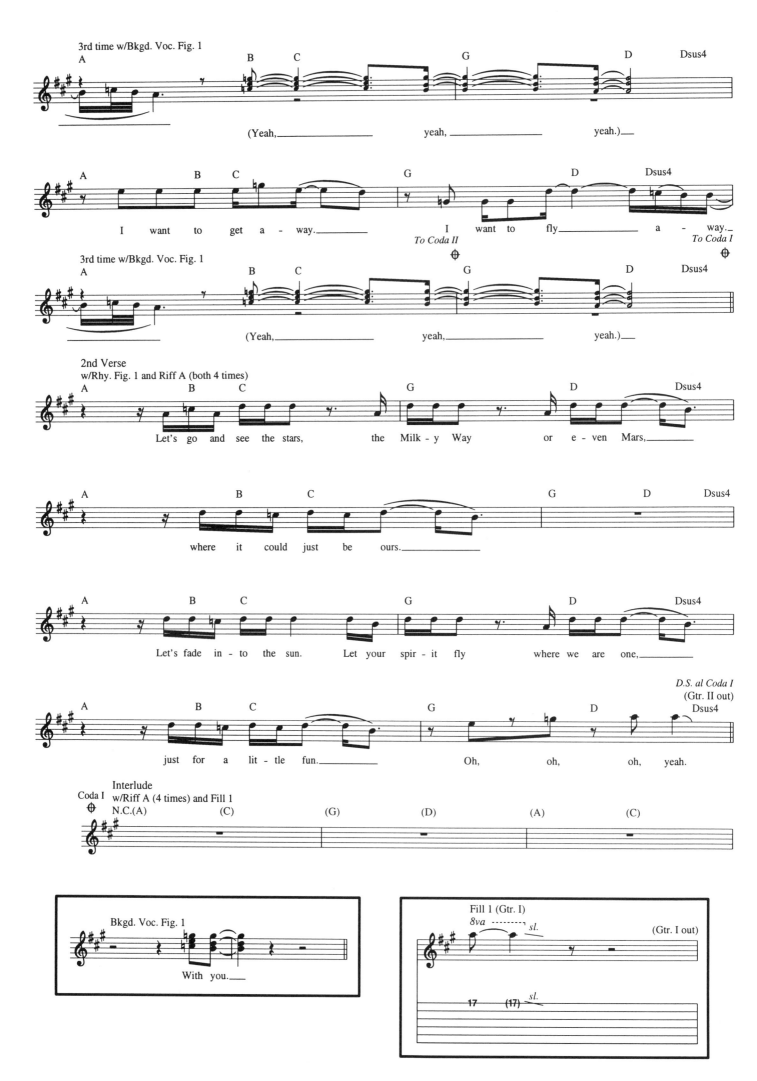

(Spoken:) I got-ta get a-way. Girl, I got-ta

D.S. al Coda II

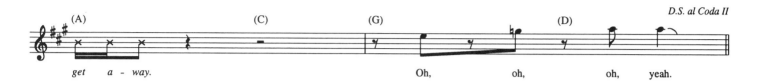

get a-way. Oh, oh, oh, yeah.

Coda II

(w/last bar of Rhy. Fig. 1 and Bkgd. Voc. Fig. 1) w/Rhy. Fig. 1 (8 times)

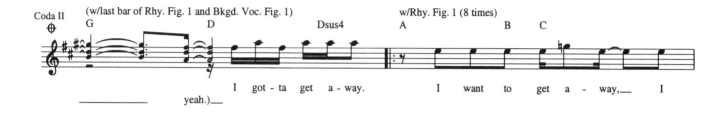

I got-ta get a-way. I want to get a-way,__ I

yeah.)__

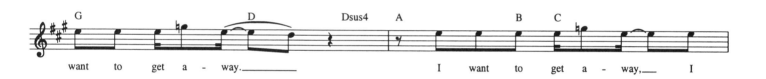

want to get a-way.__ I want to get a-way,__ I

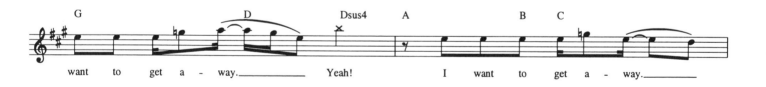

want to get a-way.__ Yeah! I want to get a-way.__

w/Bkgd. Voc. Fig. 1

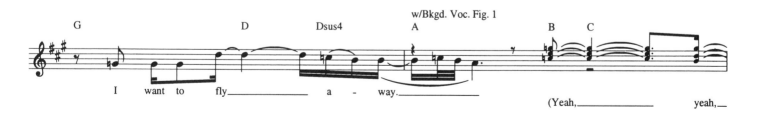

I want to fly__ a-way.__ (Yeah,__ yeah,__

Girl, I got to get a-way. Yeah, yeah, yeah, yeah, yeah.

yeah.)__ yeah.)__

13

IS THERE ANY LOVE IN YOUR HEART

Words by Lenny Kravitz
Music by Lenny Kravitz and Craig Ross

Additional Lyrics

2. Baby, baby you walk around like you own this town.
Your whole life is a fantasy, and I'm playing the clown.
You talk behind my back and spend up all my bread. *(To Chorus)*

3. Babe, you say I'm the only one, but you're fucking all my friends.
Baby, all that you care about is Gucci and Mercedes Benz.
You're just the kind that's up on all the latest trends.

IT AIN'T OVER 'TIL IT'S OVER

Words and Music by
Lenny Kravitz

*Strings arr. for gtr. Riff A is played w/slight variations ad lib when repeated or recalled (throughout).

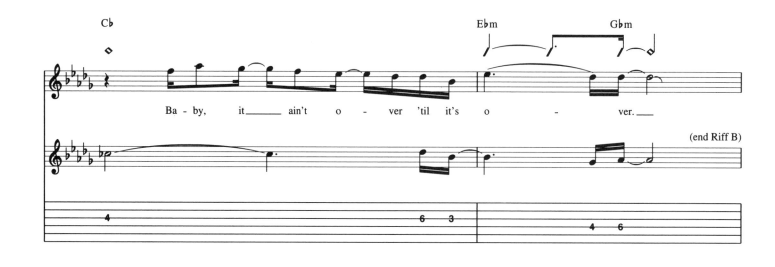

Ba - by, it___ ain't o - ver 'til it's o - ver.___

(end Riff B)

w/Riff B

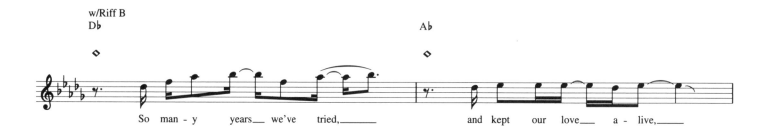

So man - y years___ we've tried,_____ and kept our love___ a - live,___

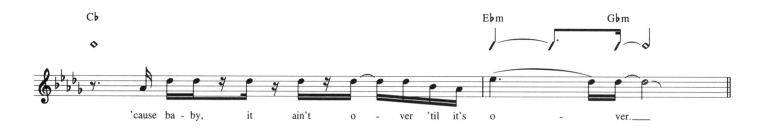

'cause ba - by, it ain't o - ver 'til it's o - ver.___

w/Rhy. Fig. 1 and Riffs A & B (all 2 times)

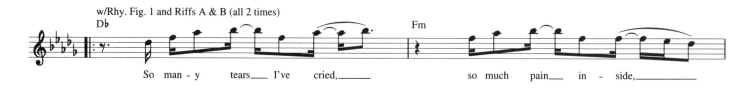

So man - y tears___ I've cried,_____ so much pain___ in - side,_____

but ba - by, it___ ain't o - ver 'til it's o - ver.___

So___ man - y years___ we've tried_____ to keep our love___ a - live,_____

Repeat and fade

'cause ba - by, it___ ain't o - ver 'til it's o - ver.___

LET LOVE RULE

Words and Music by
Lenny Kravitz

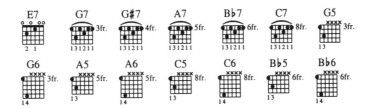

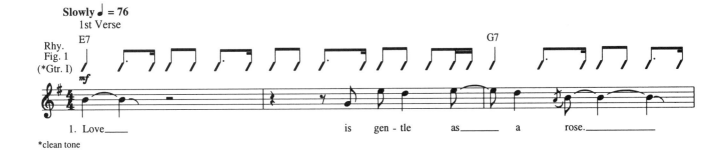

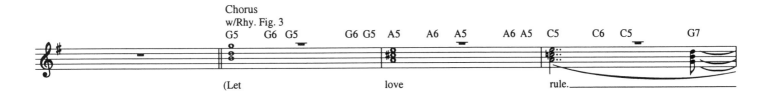

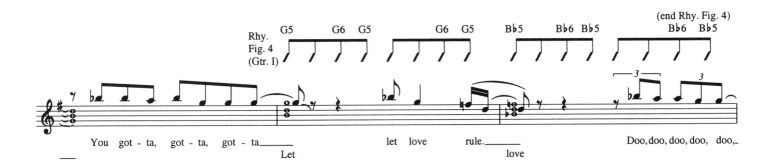

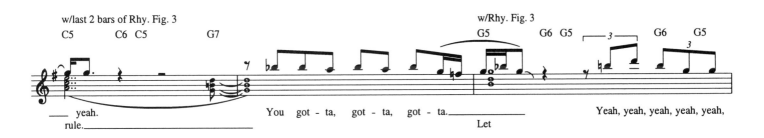

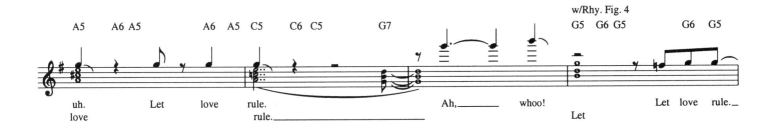

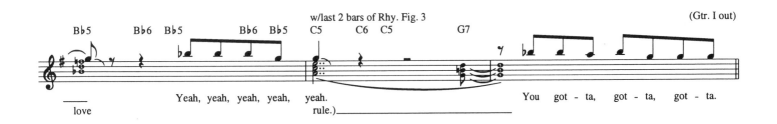

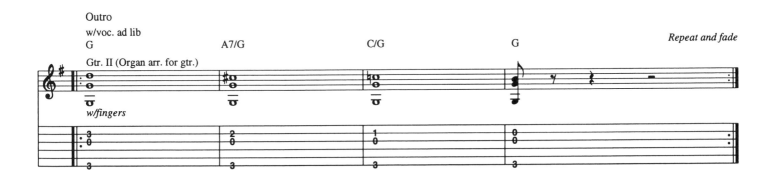

MAGDALENE

Words and Music by
Lenny Kravitz

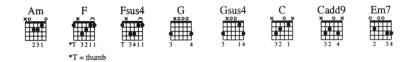

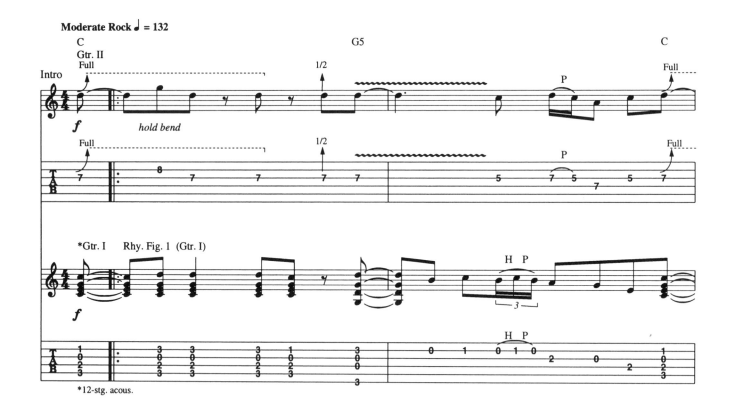

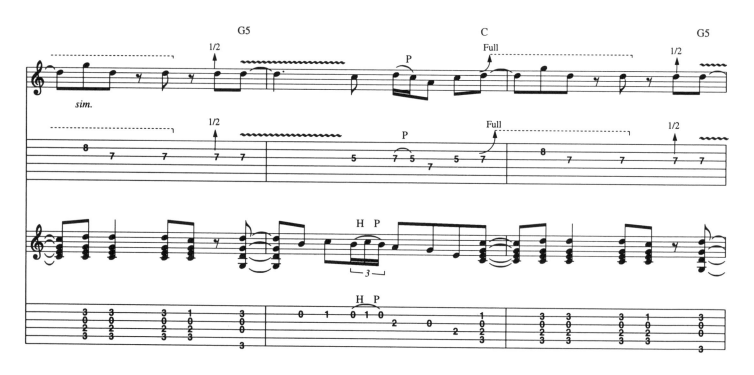

1st, 2nd Verses/Guitar solo
w/Rhy. Fig. 1

____ was on - ly sev - en - teen.____ In____ her prime of life, she was lean.____
____ was on - ly sev - en - teen.____ She packed____ her bag and went to the scene.____
3. *Guitar solo ad lib (vocal tacet)*

____ And____ her on - ly dream was to be____ on the sil - ver screen.____
____ She said,____ "I'm gon - na take on this town,____ I'm gon - na be____ the queen."____

w/Rhy. Fig. 1 (1st 7 bars only)

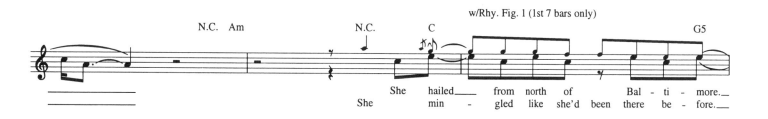

____ She hailed____ from north of Bal - ti - more.____
____ She min - gled like she'd been there be - fore.____

____ Her ma - ma said she'd end up a whore.____ And____
____ She worked____ it till they hol - lered for more.____ Then____

25

she spent up all her dough____ at the mov - ie show.____
she took off all her clothes. Now ev' - ry - bod - y knows.____
(... solo ends)

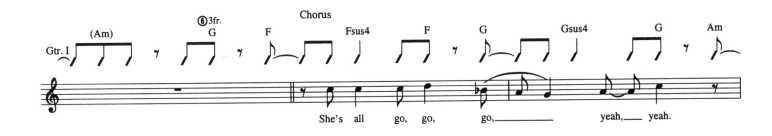

She's all go, go, go,____ yeah,____ yeah.

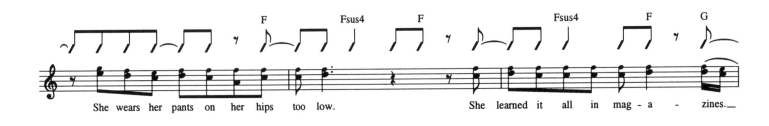

She wears her pants on her hips too low. She learned it all in mag - a - zines.___

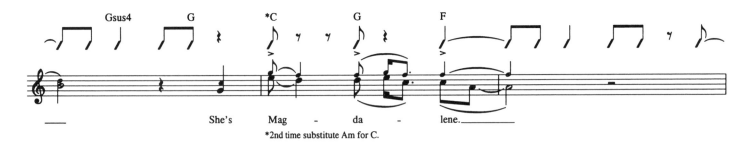

She's Mag - da - lene.____

*2nd time substitute Am for C.

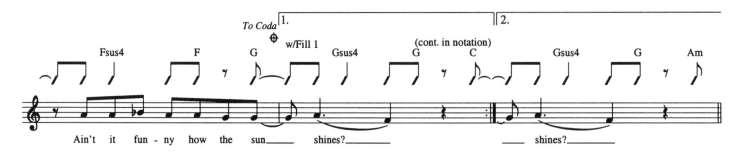

Ain't it fun - ny how the sun____ shines?____ ____ shines?____

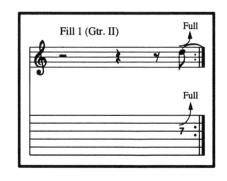

Fill 1 (Gtr. II)

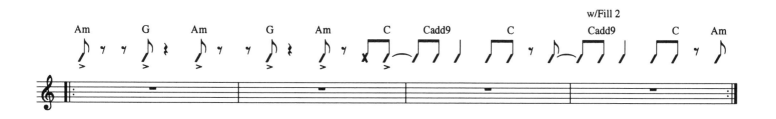

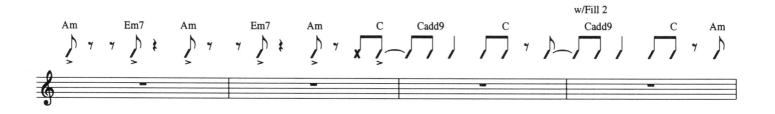

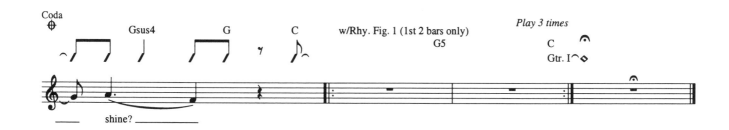

shine?

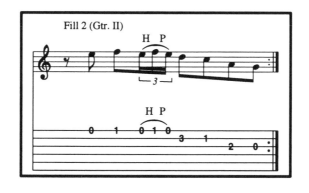

MR. CAB DRIVER

Words and Music by
Lenny Kravitz

Additional Lyrics

2. Mr. Cab Driver won't stop to pick me up.
Mr. Cab Driver I might need some help.
Mr. Cab Driver only thinks about himself.

3. Mr. Cab Driver don't like the way I look.
He don't like dreads. He thinks we're all crooks.
Mr. Cab Driver reads too many storybooks.

4. Mr. Cab Driver pass me up with eyes of fire.
Mr. Cab Driver thinks we're all 165'ers.
Mr. Cab Driver, fuck you. I'm a surviver.

MY LOVE

Words by Lenny Kravitz
Music by Lenny Kravitz and Craig Ross

Wan-na lose my mind____ in - side your head.__
Wan-na lose my mind____ in - side your bed.__

Wan-na lose it. Wan-na lose it._____ Wan-na lose my soul_ in your

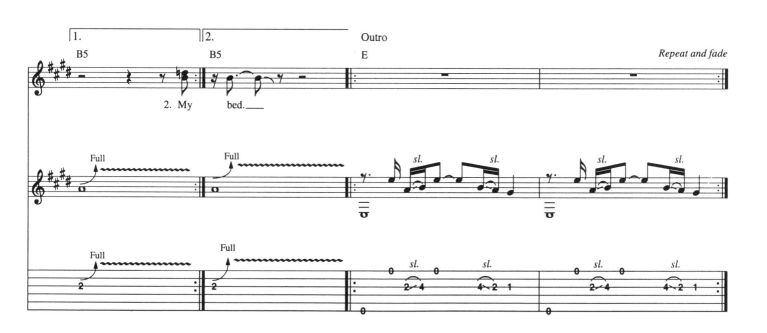

2. My bed.__

Outro

Repeat and fade

33

ROCK AND ROLL IS DEAD

Words and Music by
Lenny Kravitz

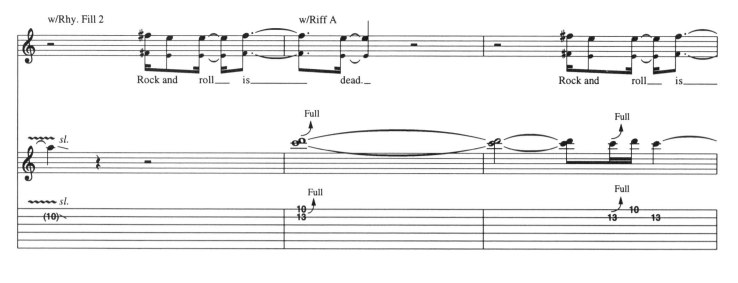

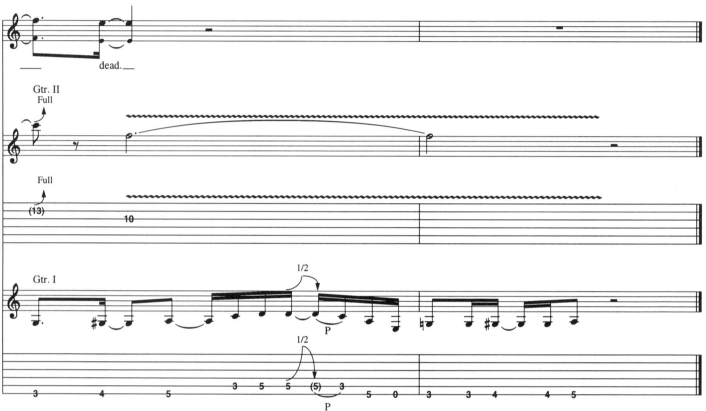

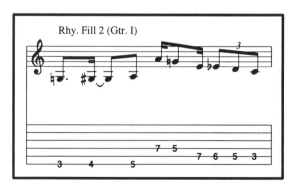

Rhy. Fill 2 (Gtr. I)

Additional Lyrics

2. You can't even sing or play an instrument
   So you just scream instead. Ooh, yeah!
   You're livin' for an image
   So you got five hundred women in your bed. Ooh, yeah!
   Rock and roll is dead.
   But it's real hard to be yourself
   When you're livin' with those demons in your head. Ooh, yeah! *(To Chorus)*

STAND BY MY WOMAN

Words by Lenny Kravitz
Music by Lenny Kravitz, Henry Hirsch,
Stephen Pasch and Anthony Krizan

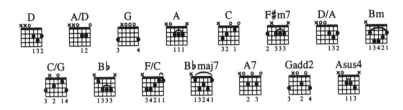

Oh, there were times__ I was-n't kind.__

And there were times__ I was-n't e - ven 'round. And there were times__ I made you cry.__

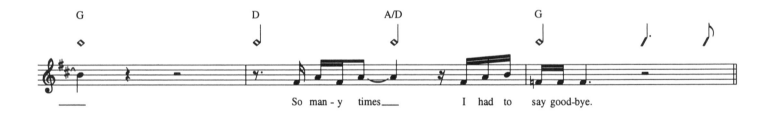

So man - y times__ I had to say good-bye.

When you want to talk, I'm on the phone.__ But now,__
But, ba - by, now I'm here for you,__ 'cause__

ba - by,__ yeah,__ I am here__ for you a - lone.__ I'm gon - na
ba - by,__ yeah,__ I am so__ in love with you.__

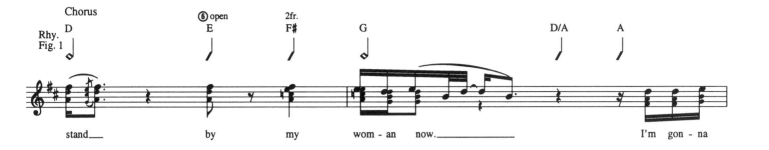

stand____ by my wom - an now._____ I'm gon - na

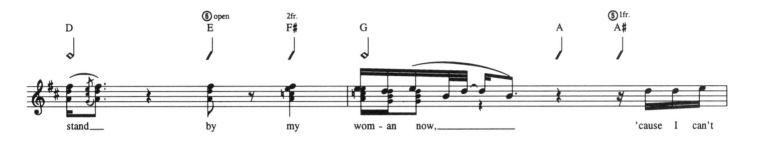

stand____ by my wom - an now,_____ 'cause I can't

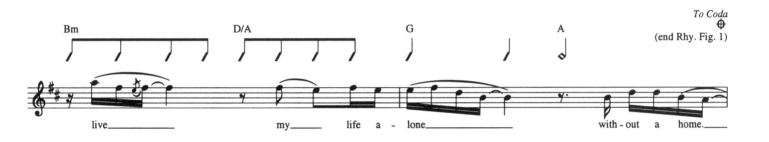

live_____ my____ life a - lone_____ with - out a home.____

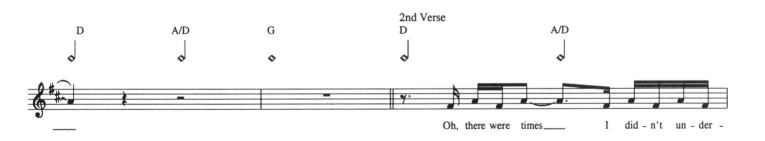

___ Oh, there were times____ I did - n't un - der -

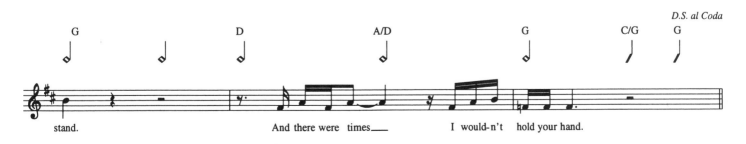

stand. And there were times____ I would-n't hold your hand.

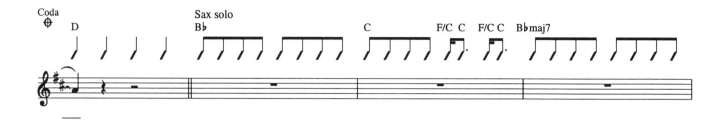

Coda

Sax solo

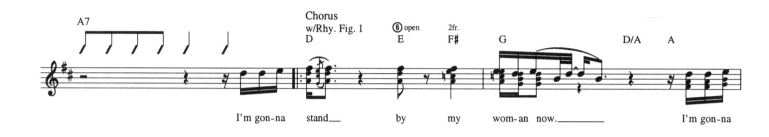

Chorus
w/Rhy. Fig. 1

I'm gon-na stand____ by my wom-an now._____ I'm gon-na

stand____ by my wom-an now,_____ 'cause_ I can't live_____ my____ life a-

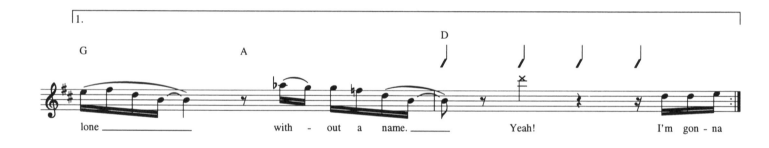

1.

lone _____ with - out a name. _____ Yeah! I'm gon - na

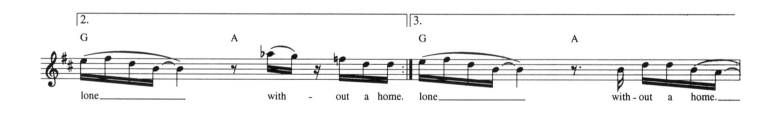

2.   3.

lone _____ with - out a home. lone_____ with - out a home.

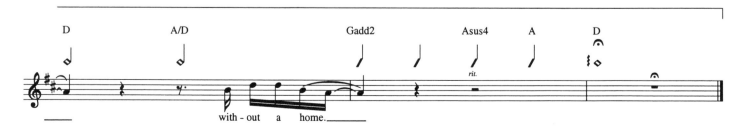

with - out a home._____

YOU'RE MY FLAVOR

Words and Music by
Lenny Kravitz

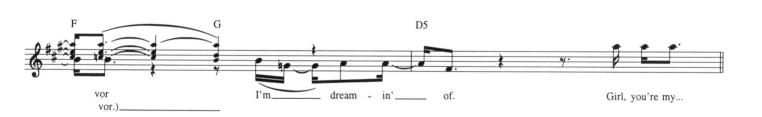

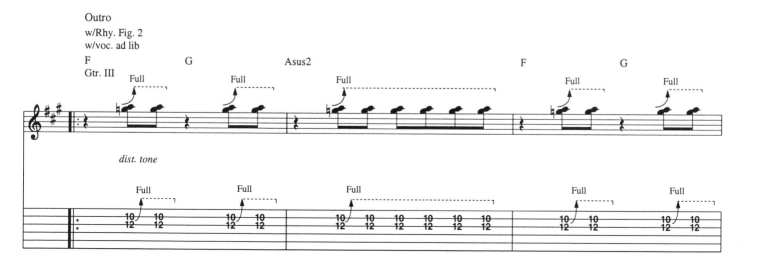

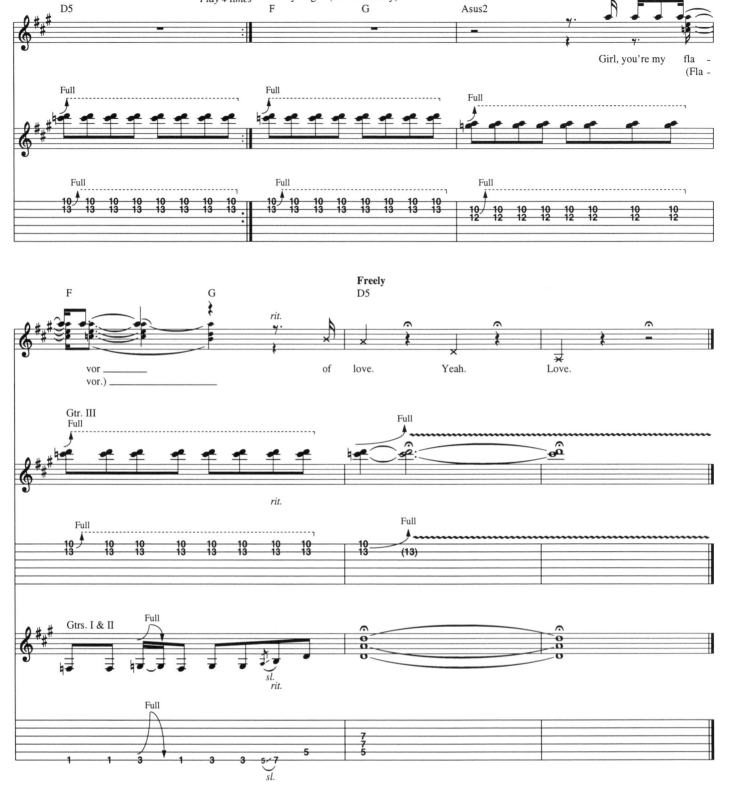

Additional Lyrics

2. The way you touch me,
   Somehow it takes away the pain.
   And now I'm a junkie,
   I'm runnin' 'round without a brain.
   I've got this jones deep inside me,
   And you are what I wanna do.
   You give me this feelin',
   You always make me feel brand-new. *(To Chorus)*

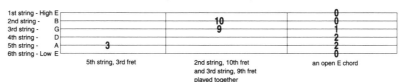

• Tablature Explanation/Notation Legend •

TABLATURE: A six-line staff that graphically represents the guitar fingerboard. By placing a number on the appropriate line, the string and the fret of any note can be indicated. For example:

```
1st string - High E
2nd string -      B                    10              0
3rd string -      G                     9              1
4th string -      D                                    2
5th string -      A        3                           2
6th string - Low  E                                    0
```

5th string, 3rd fret 2nd string, 10th fret an open E chord
and 3rd string, 9th fret
played together

Definitions for Special Guitar Notation

BEND: Strike the note and bend up a half step (one fret).

BEND: Strike the note and bend up a whole step (two frets).

BEND AND RELEASE: Strike the note and bend up a half (or whole) step, then release the bend back to the original note. All three notes are tied; only the first note is struck.

PRE-BEND: Bend the note up a half (or whole) step, then strike it.

PRE-BEND AND RELEASE: Bend the note up a half (or whole) step, strike it and release the bend back to the original note.

UNISON BEND: Strike the two notes simultaneously and bend the lower note to the pitch of the higher.

VIBRATO: Vibrate the note by rapidly bending and releasing the string with a left-hand finger.

WIDE OR EXAGGERATED VIBRATO: Vibrate the pitch to a greater degree with a left-hand finger or the tremolo bar.

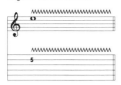

SLIDE: Strike the first note and then with the same left-hand finger move up the string to the second note. The second note is not struck.

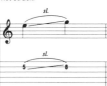

SLIDE: Same as above, except the second note is struck.

SLIDE: Slide up to the note indicated from a few frets below.

HAMMER-ON: Strike the first (lower) note, then sound the higher note with another finger by fretting it without picking.

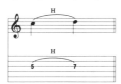

PULL-OFF: Place both fingers on the notes to be sounded. Strike the first (higher) note, then sound the lower note by pulling the finger off the higher note while keeping the lower note fretted.

TRILL: Very rapidly alternate between the note indicated and the small note shown in parentheses by hammering on and pulling off.

TAPPING: Hammer ("tap") the fret indicated with the right-hand index or middle finger and pull off to the note fretted by the left hand.

NATURAL HARMONIC: With a left-hand finger, lightly touch the string over the fret indicated, then strike it. A chime-like sound is produced.

ARTIFICIAL HARMONIC: Fret the note normally and sound the harmonic by adding the right-hand thumb edge or index finger tip to the normal pick attack.

A.H. pitch: E

TREMOLO BAR: Drop the note by the number of steps indicated, then return to original pitch.

PALM MUTE: With the right hand, partially mute the note by lightly touching the string just before the bridge.

MUFFLED STRINGS: Lay the left hand across the strings without depressing them to the fretboard; strike the strings with the right hand, producing a percussive sound.

PICK SLIDE: Rub the pick edge down the length of the string to produce a scratchy sound.

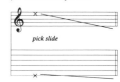

TREMOLO PICKING: Pick the note as rapidly and continuously as possible.

RHYTHM SLASHES: Strum chords in rhythm indicated. Use chord voicings found in the fingering diagrams at the top of the first page of the transcription.

SINGLE-NOTE RHYTHM SLASHES: The circled number above the note name indicates which string to play. When successive notes are played on the same string, only the fret numbers are given.